A
FOUNDATIONAL
EXPLANATION
OF
HUMAN
BEHAVIOR

How to Get Beyond Observed Behavior
to the Why of What We Do

Bartley J. Madden

ISBN: 978-0-9885969-8-6 (softcover)

ISBN: 978-0-9885969-9-3 (ebook)

INTRODUCTION

In the late 1960s, I began an intellectual journey that initially focused on improving my understanding of the connection between a firm's performance and its market valuation. In 2020, my finance work culminated with *Value Creation Principles: The Pragmatic Theory of the Firm Begins with Purpose and Ends with Sustainable Capitalism*. A major takeaway of this book is that a firm's knowledge-building proficiency primarily determines its long-term performance.

Over the same time period, I developed an ongoing passion for researching systems thinking, knowledge building, and human behavior (psychology). And more specifically, I have been promoting a structural reform of the FDA regulatory process through journal articles, op-eds, and my book *Free to Choose Medicine: Better Drugs Sooner at Lower Cost*, which was instrumental in Japan's passage in 2014 of early, informed access to regenerative medicine drugs—an application of systems thinking.[1]

System thinkers, and other readers, might find useful the phrase *fulcrum insight* designating a stake-in-the-ground causal relationship which can deliver a substantial system improvement and is not context dependent. For FDA reform, the fulcrum insight is that clarity about the appropriate system goal plus elevating the key constraint equals substantial performance gains.[2] The con-

---

1. Bartley J. Madden. 2020. *"Science* on FDA Liberalization: A Response to the Status Quo Process for Medical Treatments." *Econ Journal Watch* 17(1): 90–97. This article explains how Free to Choose Medicine would accelerate innovation to the benefit of patients in any country that currently relies on an FDA-type regulatory system.

2. See the discussion of Eli Goldratt's Theory of Constraints in Bartley J. Madden. 2020. *Value Creation Principles: The Pragmatic Theory of the Firm Begins with Purpose and Ends with Sustainable Capitalism*. Hoboken, NJ: John Wiley & Sons, Chapter 3.

ventional goal of safe and effective drugs leads to a relentless demand for ever more expensive clinical testing demands, sky-high prescription drug prices, and, importantly, delayed access to life-changing medical treatments. I argue that the appropriate goal is better drugs, sooner, at lower cost. The key constraint is the hugely expensive (time and money) FDA clinical testing process.

In contrast to insights that can generate small incremental gains for a specified context, fulcrum insights can lead to large-scale value creation across many contexts. For example, Hernando de Soto cogently argues for a way to accelerate economic growth in the least-developed countries by formalizing legal property rights for houses, land, and businesses while minimizing bureaucratic obstacles to starting and running businesses. He explains: "... their assets are dead capital ... The poor inhabitants of these nations—five-sixths of humanity—do have things, but they lack the process to represent their property and create capital. They have houses but not titles; crops but not deeds; businesses but not statutes of incorporation."[3] De Soto's fulcrum insight would create capital for those most in need while also enabling them to be value creators and participants in the global capitalistic system.

My current project is to craft a book about improving system performance that plows new ground compared to *Value Creation Principles*. These two books (and related upcoming videos) will offer business schools an educational package for use in class or as part of an open online course. The working title for the new book is *Fulcrum Insights: How You Can Generate Big Ideas to Elevate System Performance*. This book is in the initial stage of research/writing and will have seven chapters that correspond to the seven steps to improve performance as outlined in Figure 1.

---

3. Hernando de Soto. 2000. *The Mystery of Capital: Why Capitalism Triumphs in the West and Fails Everywhere Else*. New York: Basic Books, pp. 6–7.

Figure 1:
A systematic approach to improving system performance

SEVEN STEPS TO IMPROVE SYSTEM PERFORMANCE

(1) Gain clarity as to why people behave as they do – become comfortable with a foundational explanation of human behavior.

↓

(2) Develop an inventory of fulcrum insights – important, context-free causal relationships.

↓

(3) Understand the system that is targeted for improvement, including categorization as ordinary, complicated, complex, or chaotic, and apply cause and effect analysis wherever applicable in order to reveal the source of divergent views concerning change.

↓

(4) Discover the assumptions, often hidden by language, that may hold the key to unraveling complexity and gaining a more insightful understanding of core problems.

↓

(5) Use your imagination, including the application of fulcrum insights, to develop novel connections that may yield significant innovations.

↓

(6) Orchestrate feedback and experiment with provisional innovations to change the system.

↓

(7) Fully understand the objections to change, then overcome these objections and monitor how the changed system performs.

The above seven steps differ from performance improvement approaches described in many popular books on management, innovation, and creativity. In contrast to the frequently encountered new management idea that soon becomes a fad, these seven steps represent a systematic thinking process to be used in all contexts. Moreover, the explanatory chapters will provide novel ideas, document relevant academic thinking, and illustrate tie-ins to real-world system improvements, especially in business. The best tools for those who begin a journey to use and improve the ideas distilled into the above seven steps are curiosity, skepticism, imagination, humility, perseverance, and a passion for pragmatism.

A Foundational Understanding of Human Behavior addresses Step 1. I hope to convince you to adopt Perceptual Control Theory (PCT) as the foundational explanation of human behavior—why we act in the ways we do. Over many years, I have studied myriad PCT books and journal articles. As questions concerned me, I have been fortunate to get answers from the leading researchers, including Bill Powers who first developed PCT. The book in your hands analyzes the work of Bill Powers and his colleagues in developing PCT and shows its wide application.

Many readers currently view human behavior as responses to stimuli (e.g., carrots-and-sticks management approach often seen in business and a form of behaviorism) and/or believe that our brain plans in detail with incredible speed every action to deal with disturbances in the environment, i.e., cognitive psychology. In this book, a strong case is made that these approaches are decidedly inferior to PCT.

We human beings live *purposeful* lives which can easily be ignored with a stimulus-response approach to understanding human behavior. Due to a continual stream of environmental disturbances, actions are varied in order to cancel the effects of these disturbances on our perceptions of controlled (important to our goals) variables. PCT provides a fundamental fulcrum insight: behavior is the control of perception. The purpose of this book is to get you comfortable with this insight and excited about putting it to practical use.

A
FOUNDATIONAL
EXPLANATION
OF
HUMAN
BEHAVIOR

You [William T. Powers] did not invent the [negative feedback] loop. It existed in a few mechanical devices in antiquity, and came to engineering fruition when electrical devices became common. Some psychologists even wrote about "feedback." But the manner in which living organisms make use of the feedback loop—or I could say the manner in which the feedback loop enabled living creatures to come into being—that insight is yours alone. That insight by itself should be sufficient to put you down on the pages of the history books as the founder of the science of psychology.

—*Philip J. Runkel* [4]

4. Dag Forssell (ed.). 2010. *Dialogue Concerning the Two Chief Approaches to a Science of Life*. Menlo Park, CA: Living Control Systems Publishing, p. 497.

MAINSTREAM PSYCHOLOGY IGNORES PERCEPTUAL CONTROL THEORY (PCT)

The type of system addressed in my forthcoming book, *Fulcrum Insights,* entails coordinated activities in which people work to achieve a specified goal or purpose. This can range from a small team to a large, complex organization. Systems involve people on the inside and on the outside (e.g., a manufacturing plant and its outside suppliers or a classroom using books written by outside authors). Moreover, management may have divergent views of how to make changes in order to improve performance. Is it not reasonable that a prerequisite to system analysis should be clarifying why we act in the ways we do? I believe this is one of those patently "obvious" ideas. So much has been written about performance improvement that intimately involves people, but totally absent, or inadequately treated, is a foundational explanation of human behavior.

Cognitive psychology textbooks introduce the power of our brains as calculating engines to issue commands to our muscles to respond to environmental stimuli. Even though cognitive psychology has replaced behaviorism, which ignored brain functioning, the basic sequence of a cause (stimulus) followed by an effect (response) is maintained. The cognitive revolution began in the 1950s as an interdisciplinary study of how the brain uses sensory inputs to guide behavior. The early developers of cognitive science believed that the brain acted as a computer that models the external environment and instantaneously calculates an appropriate response to a stimulus just experienced. This approach facilitates the stimulus/response framework that many find appealing because it seems to reflect common sense. This linear (straight line) approach is extraordinarily useful for explaining the behavior of nonliving things such as billiard balls. The mass, velocity, and direction of the impacting ball (stimulus) can be used to predict the subsequent velocity and direction (response) of the impacted ball.

In 1960, the first PCT journal articles began an intellectual movement that can potentially become a paradigm change regarding a theory of human behavior. Perceptual Control Theory asserts that, for living organisms such as people, it is misleading to view their actions (behavior) as a response to a stimulus. For example, imagine driving a car in the rain on a windy day. The external environment is continually disturbing your driving via a multitude of stimuli. Do you continually respond using your brain to model the condition of the road, the wind speed, the weight of the car, the grip of your tires (new versus old), etc., and then send signals through your nervous system to activate muscles to adjust the steering wheel in the calculated manner? A more plausible PCT-based explanation is that behavior is control of perception, as described by William T. Powers,[5] the developer of PCT. We humans are wired as hierarchical control systems (see Figure 2).

Instead of linear cause and effect, we experience life as a closed loop where cause and effect interact continuously. At any point in time, your perception of the position of the car between lane markers can be disturbed, causing you to act almost instantly (move the steering wheel) which immediately restores your perception close to what you want it to be. This process is ongoing with new environmental conditions leading to new steering wheel adjustments. We have a closed loop of cause and effect. With a closed loop, actions impact what is sensed, which in turn impacts subsequent action. The human system controls what it perceives and not what it does. In the late 1800s, both William James and John Dewey got it right about behavior as control of perception with a closed loop of cause and effect.

In his 1890 textbook, *Principles of Psychology,* James noted the actions of nonliving things for which linear cause and

---

5. See William T. Powers, "The World According to PCT," in Warren Mansell (ed.). 2020. *The Interdisciplinary Handbook of Perceptual Control Theory.* London: Academic Press, Chapter 1.

effect suffices. He contrasted human behavior to how a magnet attracts filings (see Figure 3) which does not change if an obstruction (a card) is placed between the magnet and the filings.

Figure 2:
The difference between nonliving things and living organisms

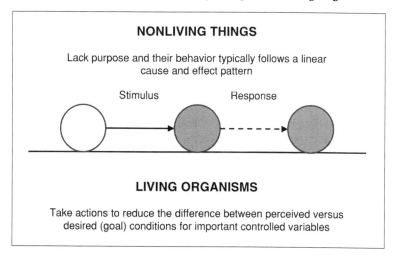

Figure 3:
Linear causation

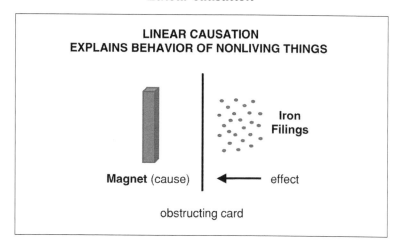

In contrast, James described in his textbook a situation involving Romeo and Juliet:

> Romeo wants Juliet as filings want a magnet; and if no obstacles intervene, he moves toward her by as straight a line as they [can manage]. But Romeo and Juliet, if a wall be built between them, do not remain idiotically pressing their faces against its opposite sides like the magnet and the filings with [an obstructing] card. Romeo soon finds a circuitous way, by scaling the wall or otherwise, of touching Juliet's lips directly. With the filings, the path is fixed; whether it reaches the end depends on accidents. With the lover it is the end which is fixed, the path may be modified indefinitely.[6]

The above insight is the essence of PCT focused on purposeful behavior which involves overcoming obstructions that interfere with achieving one's goals. Why didn't the discipline of psychology incorporate this insight? Richard Marken and Timothy Carey, leading PCT researchers, explain that psychologists are typically uncomfortable with abandoning the temporal sequence of an explicit cause leading in a fixed linear manner to an explicit effect and that psychologists invent many different theories to explain purposeful behavior in linear cause-and-effect terms. Marken and Carey point out:

> Romeo's apparently purposeful pursuit of Juliet [may be] seen as being *caused* by Juliet's attractiveness just as the iron filings' apparently purposeful pursuit of the magnet is *caused* by the magnet's force field. But this cause-effect explanation of purposeful behavior works only if you ignore the part of James's parable about dealing with obstructions to goal achievement. Romeo finds

---

6. William James. 1890. *Principles of Psychology*. Chicago: University of Chicago, p. 4. (1952 edition).

a circuitous way around the obstructions, the filings don't. Juliet's attractiveness can no more *cause* Romeo to get around an obstructing wall than the magnetic field can cause the filings to get around the obstructing card.[7]

To summarize, in a steady-state environment without continual disturbances, a psychological hypothesis that asserts an explicit cause (e.g., Juliet's attractiveness) to apparently explain what Romeo does can appear plausible. And Juliet's attractiveness (cause) comes before Romeo's actions (effect) thereby maintaining the conventional notion of a cause preceding an effect. But, if it is assumed that Juliet's attractiveness truly causes an explicit effect, is it not odd that Romeo seems to care little about which action he takes and a lot more about whether it gets him what he wants? What is important to Romeo is achieving his goal, not how he does it. Unlike the iron filings, living organisms can use a variety of means to get what they want. **The PCT explanation that applies to human behavior is that a person acts to keep the perception of a controlled variable as close as possible to the desired or reference state. Behavior is the control of perception.** Technically, a perception refers to a sensory stimulation that gives rise to a perceptual signal (neural current) in the brain, which represents some aspect of the outside world. Practically, a perception is what we experience, e.g., tasting of strawberry ice cream or seeing a friend walk across the room. Romeo is fundamentally trying to get his actual perception to match his reference state—his lips experiencing the touch of Juliet's lips.

Figure 4 illustrates how easy (and misleading) it is to label what we see in terms of linear cause and effect.

---

7. Richard S. Marken and Timothy A. Carey. 2015. *Controlling People: The Paradoxical Nature of Being Human.* Samford Valley, Australia: Australian Academic Press, p. 24; italics added.

Figure 4:
Romeo and Juliet

ASSUMED LINEAR CAUSATION LEADS TO A SUPERFICIAL EXPLANATION OF BEHAVIOR

Juliet's
attractiveness
is the apparent
cause

The **effect**
appears to be
Romeo
attempting to
climb the wall

- It is misleading to conclude that a particular observed effect must follow the apparent cause.

- Romeo could take many different actions to get what he wants.

- The observed behavior could significantly change if Romeo's reference state for the controlled variable changed.

Extending this example further, suppose that Romeo discovered that Juliet had been unfaithful to him, and the next day his reference state was to keep "far away" from her. How well would the "attractiveness" variable then explain Romeo's indifference to get close to Juliet? Perhaps the conclusion is that stimulus/response empirical findings are context dependent and not representative of a foundational theory of human behavior.

We return to the idea of a closed loop of cause and effect where actions for adjusting a steering wheel or for Romeo to surmount some obstacle involve a continual dance of controlling what is perceived.

Along these lines, in 1896 John Dewey, with his typical wisdom, addressed the need for a sound foundation for psychology:

What we have is a circuit [closed loop], not an arc or broken segment of a circle. This circuit is more truly termed organic than reflex, because the motor response determines the stimulus, just as truly as sensory stimulus determines movement.[8]

Figure 5 illustrates the closed-loop concept.

Figure 5:
Closed-loop causation

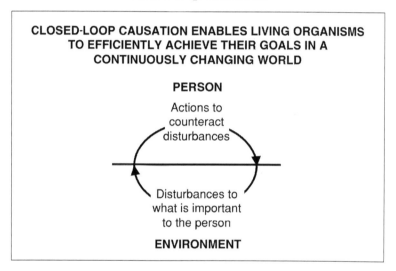

CLOSED-LOOP CAUSATION ENABLES LIVING ORGANISMS TO EFFICIENTLY ACHIEVE THEIR GOALS IN A CONTINUOUSLY CHANGING WORLD

PERSON

Actions to counteract disturbances

Disturbances to what is important to the person

ENVIRONMENT

Here is an important takeaway: what we do (system output) invariably impacts what we perceive (system input). While the closed loop of causation is easily visualized for driving a car, even those behavioral situations that appear to be linear cause and effect are still better explained using a closed-loop viewpoint. Keep in mind that the particular effect you observe is one of many possibilities. And the observed effect can vanish if a person changes (not visibly to you) their reference state for the controlled variable.

---

8. John Dewey. 1896. "The Reflex Arc in Psychology." *Psychological Review* 3(4) 357–370.

PCT APPLIED TO LIVING ORGANISMS

Building on the work of Claude Bernhard, Walter Cannon's 1932 book, *The Wisdom of the Body*, developed the concept of *homeostasis*, which focuses on how key variables such as body temperature and blood sugar levels are automatically maintained within narrow ranges despite continual disturbances. The key is negative feedback control of the physiological processes that control life-maintaining conditions inside the (system) body. A case can be made that this enabled species survival and their subsequent evolution.[9] That human beings control continual outside disturbances with negative feedback loops should not be surprising.

The extraordinary utility of the negative feedback loop for living organisms is evident in how the bacterium *Escherichia coli* (*E. coli*) navigates. Marken and Powers built a PCT model with negative feedback that replicated its behavior. They also showed that human subjects, when their locomotion was restricted to mimic *E. coli*, behaved consistently with the negative feedback model.

> The biased random-walk chemotaxis [movement] of the bacterium *Escherichia coli* is a remarkably effective method of navigation based on random trial-and-error responding rather than steering. Humans restricted to the same mode of responding are able to navigate to target locations, just like the bacterium. *This mode of navigation can be modeled as an input control process that selectively retains favorable and rejects unfavorable consequences of the random responses.* The selection process is determined by the internal organization of the system rather than the

---

9. For insights about the behavior of animals consistent with PCT principles, see Louise Barrett. 2011. *Beyond the Brain: How Body and Environment Shape Animal and Human Minds*. Princeton, NJ: Princeton University Press, Chapter 6.

external influence of the environment (as in natural selection or reinforcement).[10]

While today's psychology textbooks discuss purpose (goal/ motivation), they invariably focus on statistical averages (gross tendencies). These textbooks lack PCT's rigorous and comprehensive explanation of how an *individual person* achieves (or tries to achieve) his or her purposes. How did this come about?

The insights of William James and John Dewey for living organisms, such as people, were shelved most likely because a workable theory was not available at that time. Bill Powers began developing PCT in the 1950s, and, as previously noted, he first sketched out these ideas in articles in 1960. He thoroughly explained PCT in a 1973 book.[11]

Meanwhile, the discipline of psychology marched behind the flag of the *scientific method:* develop a hypothesis, rigorously define variables, test how the hypothetical cause correlates with the observed effect, and verify that findings can be replicated. The scientific approach led to continuing expansion of knowledge in the physical sciences focused on nonliving things. For their empirical research, mainstream psychologists adopted the scientific method with independent variables manipulated by the experimenter and correlated with dependent variables. When researchers use a regression equation with a dependent variable and independent variables, they are accepting linear causation.

---

10. Richard S. Marken and William T. Powers. 1989. *"Random-Walk Chemotaxis: Trial and Error as a Control Process." Behavioral Neuroscience* 103(6): 1348–1355; italics added.

11. W. T. Powers, R. K. Clark, and R. L. McFarland. 1960. "A general feedback theory of human behavior. Part I." *Perceptual & Motor Skills* 11: 71–88. W. T. Powers, R. K. Clark, and R. L. McFarland. 1960. "A general feedback theory of human behavior. Part II." *Perceptual & Motor Skills* 11: 309–323; and William T. Powers. 1973. *Behavior: The Control of Perception.* New Canaan, CT: Benchmark Publications (2nd edition, 2005).

Let's return to the situation where Romeo was trying to get his perception of the controlled variable to match the reference state. This is the inside view which contravenes the outside view of attempting to explain Romeo's behavior by *observing what he does*. After learning about Juliet's unfaithfulness, Romeo's reference state for closeness to Juliet radically changed. His subsequent behavior may seem strange to an observer familiar with his past behavior toward Juliet. Powers summarized this situation as follows:

> [Perceptual] control theory bypasses the entire set of empirical problems in psychology concerning how people tend to behave under various external circumstances. One kind of behavior can appear under many different circumstances; instead of comparing all the various kinds of causes with each other while looking for objective similarities to explain the common effects, we are led by control theory to look for the *inputs* that are disturbed not only by the discovered causes but by all possible causes. For a thousand unconnected empirical generalizations based on superficial similarities among stimuli, I here substitute one general underlying principle: *control of input.*[12]

Ignoring control of input and singularly focusing on observed behavior (output) is the crux of what Powers called the behavioral illusion. Consider a very cold winter day when your daughter embarks on a cause-and-effect experiment for her psychology class. Whenever a person leaves your home's front door open for at least two minutes, she observes that this *causes* the furnace to pump hot air (effect) into the adjacent room. This empirical finding is repeatedly replicated by your daughter until she encounters

---

12. William T. Powers. 1978. "Quantitative Analysis of Purposive Systems: Some Spadework at the Foundation of Scientific Psychology." *Psychological Review* 85(5): 417–435.

a failure. Since empirical studies in the social sciences seek general tendencies, her average relationship is strong even though one observation shows no effect following the cause. What actually occurred is that, unknown to your daughter, your mischievous son lowered the thermostat setting from 70 degrees to 40 degrees. Consequently, opening the front door was not immediately followed by the furnace pumping hot air. Stimulus-response analysis will fail to provide an insightful understanding when a system operates with a controlled variable.

This example is useful, at one level, because it deals, in a commonsense way, with a thermostat setting (reference state) and the perception of the controlled variable (room temperature). However, its oversimplification includes an outside observer being able to see and adjust the reference state (thermostat setting). For living organisms, outsiders can't see the organism's reference state and typically are not even aware of what the controlled variable is, and this lack of knowledge is magnified when multiple control variables are operating. Engineering control systems differ from living organisms because the users can set the reference (desired) values.

Consider the situation where a person points out to you that their teenager just put a jacket on *because* the weather turned cold. With a PCT mindset, you think to yourself what is truly happening. The teenager put a jacket on in order to *experience* warmth; more specifically, she took action to get her skin temperature (controlled variable) close to the reference state for that particular sensory perception. She could have entered a car or a house if that were the more expeditious route to experience warmth—variable means for a fixed end, as William James explained a long time ago.

I recently gulped a glass of water after taking an initial sip of some exceedingly spicy soup. (You know where this is going.) Did the soup "cause" my immediate swallowing of water? Some readers might push back and argue that, as a practical matter, I would not have gulped the water were it not for the very spicy soup. However, this represents a superficial explanation of behavior. The PCT explanation travels well for changing contexts; i.e., it represents a foundational understanding of human behavior. Example: my wife had the same soup and didn't blink. She grew up in a wonderful Mexican family and she was accustomed to enjoying eating red jalapeno peppers, which affect me like swallowing a small blowtorch. Concerning soup, my (desired) reference state for perception of food temperature on my tongue is considerably lower than my wife's. The important point is that, in contrast to empirical studies with regression-derived statistics for central tendencies, **PCT explains how an individual person behaves and enables mathematical models to be constructed that can replicate specific types of behavior—a benefit not available to theories in psychology which lack PCT's precision.**

BOARDING THE PCT TRAIN

Boarding the PCT train requires that you check off on six critical insights—they work best as a package helping you put together the major pieces of the PCT puzzle.

#1. A prerequisite to gaining insights about human behavior is to understand what control means. Otherwise, one is likely to view behavior as a repeating sequence of stimulus-response and be satisfied with what mistakenly appears to be commonsense logic. As noted earlier, this leads to a superficial understanding of human behavior. In contrast to nonliving things, we live purposeful lives, which is to say we continually try to get what we want in a world of continual change, which yields disturbances that potentially move us away from what we want.

In a very real sense, at any point in time, what we know about the world is what we perceive through our senses.

These perceptions are guideposts that inform us as to how close we are to what we want. We act (behave) to control what we perceive as important to us. That's it—behavior is the control of perception, which is the title to Bill Powers' 1973 book. Control is maintaining a perceived variable at a reference or desired state in spite of continual disturbances.

Language matters. Once we begin using precise language for control and behavior, we have checked off an important step in understanding human behavior.

#2. We humans are living control systems that function with closed-loop causation. As pointed out earlier, with closed-loop causation, what the (human) system does impacts what it senses and what it senses impacts what it subsequently does. However, closed-loop causation happens so automatically that it can be missed. You turn your head to better see something of interest and the action of turning your head affects visual perception and subsequent action, and so it goes: closed-loop causation all day long. With circular closed-loop causation, we can't speak of an independent cause of behavior.

#3. Open-loop (linear) cause-and-effect (stimulus-response) thinking is highly useful in areas ranging from manufacturing processes to the physical sciences; however, one needs to shift to closed-loop-PCT thinking when analyzing the behavior of an individual person. Knowing when to use open-loop or closed-loop thinking requires an especially clear understanding of how control differs from a stimulus-response process. Let's begin with Figure 6.

Figure 6 displays a stimulus as the input to the nervous system, followed by a response or output from the system. This is linear cause-and-effect logic in which the stimulus, after a time lag, is followed by a response. Cause precedes effect.

In Figure 6, the stimulus is labeled "disturbance" and the response is labeled "action" to conform to PCT terminology. A single response is shown although if many people experience a particular stimulus, expect different responses dependent upon the specific environment coupled with people having different controlled variables and different reference states (Powers preferred the term "reference signal").[13]

Figure 6:
Stimulus-response worldview

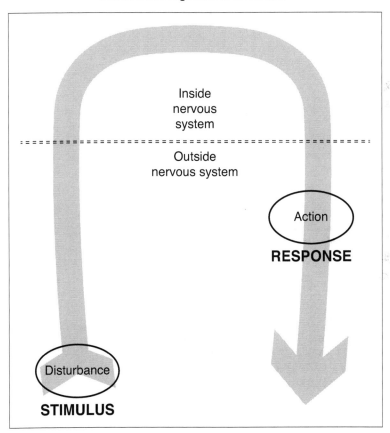

---

13. The observed response(s) to a particular stimulus tend to be specific to the environmental context. Consequently, with a stable control system the outside environment, as opposed to what takes place inside the person, is likely to have the most influence on the response(s).

If you happen to observe a person's response following a particular stimulus, is it not easy (assuming that you never learned about PCT) to think that the stimulus "caused" the response (action)? Absolutely, which is why linear causation is so popular with explanations of behavior. We see what's easy to see. What observers fail to see is the person's control system because it is not visible. This is inside the nervous system, whereas the visible stimulus and the response are outside the nervous system (see Figure 6).

The existence of a control system invalidates a stimulus being the cause of an observed response. What actually is happening is that when the disturbance affects a person's controlled variable (discussed later), that causes action to be taken to get the controlled variable back to a desired state. The action taken is not a response to the disturbance (stimulus) even though it is easy to conclude so. In fact, if an environmental disturbance had no effect on a person's controlled variables, then no response results.

#4. The key to understanding control is to understand how a negative feedback loop functions. The result is a sharpened intuition about PCT and an appreciation for the preciseness of PCT that allows for researchers to build computational models. An iterative process of model building and evaluation of how well the model corresponds to actual human behavior is the same learning process that has generated progress in the physical sciences. The loop is *negative* because actions taken *reduce* the existing error, as illustrated in Figure 7, and move the system to being in control (approximate zero error).[14]

---

14. Figures 7, 8, 9, and 11 were originally crafted by Dag Forssell and have been slightly modified by me. Reprinted with permission from Living Control Systems Publishing, which contains a treasure trove of PCT books, papers, and programs, most of which are free downloads. The figures were published in Dag Forssell (ed.). 2010. *Dialogue Concerning the Two Chief Approaches to a Science of Life*. Menlo Park, CA: Living Control Systems Publishing, pp. xxiii and xxiv.

Figure 7:
Negative feedback loop

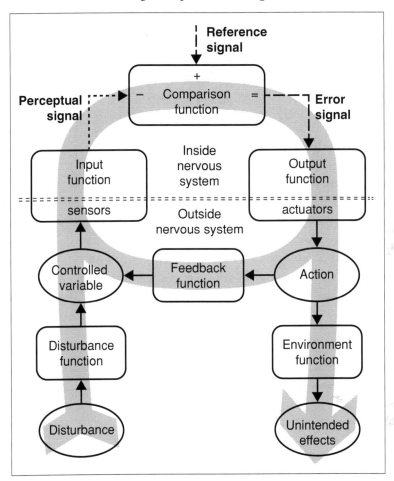

Let's describe Figure 7 beginning with the *controlled variable*. As I am writing these words, one of my controlled variables is my sensory perception of noise level. My wife has turned on the TV in the adjacent room and the resulting noise represents a *disturbance* to the desired state of my controlled variable. That noise reaches my ears via a *disturbance function* that determines what I actually sense (e.g., the walls of my office dampen the noise).

Inside my ears, the noise is sensed and the *input function* translates this sensed perception into a neural signal. This perceptual signal is one of two key inputs to the *comparison function*. The other input is the *reference signal*, which is my preferred environmental noise level while writing in my office. The difference between my current perception versus my preferred state (reference signal) represents an error that becomes a neural signal transmitted to the *output function*. It guides actuators (e.g., muscles) to initiate *action*, which can be ramped up (loop gain) to handle large errors. The purpose of the action undertaken is to move the controlled variable (noise perception) back to my desired state. The *feedback function* translates action into a new perception. In this situation, I closed my office door, thereby achieving my desired state and reducing error to zero. An action often produces *unintended effects* via the *environment function*. In this case, the environment in my office changed (now quiet); however, if my wife calls out for me to meet someone at our condo elevator, with the office door closed, I'll likely not hear her.

The loop from the controlled variable to the comparison function to action is a negative feedback loop because actions taken are intended to reduce error and keep the system in control, i.e., controlled variable matches desired state. This simple illustration hints at the intrinsic speed and efficiency in which negative feedback loops maintain control. The earlier discussion of driving a car provides a useful picture of the speed and efficiency of the negative feedback loop that employs a circular or closed loop of causation. The sensed perception of lane position leads to a comparison with the reference signal and any error gets translated into an action of our hands moving the steering wheel. Hence, what we sense affects what we do and what we do affects what we sense, in a circular fashion.

The key to the PCT-version of control theory is the negative feedback loop, which Powers referred to as the basic principle of life.[15] The conventional view of behavior as "control" of actions needs to be replaced with PCT showing that the consequences of actions are actually controlled. In other words, a control system does not control actions; rather, the system controls what it senses. Getting comfortable with the prior sentence is another checkmark in understanding human behavior.

#5. Behaviorism, which is rooted in a stimulus-response view, lacks PCT's parsimonious and powerful theoretical underpinning which can explain so much with negative feedback, closed-loop causation, hierarchical control systems (discussed later), and computational models that employ mathematical precision in place of the vague language so typical of mainstream psychology.

In the early 1900s, John B. Watson argued that the focus of mainstream psychology on introspection was mistaken, interfering with predictions about human behavior that could be evaluated experimentally. In an influential article, "Psychology as the Behaviorist Views It," Watson asserted:

> Psychology, as the behaviorist views it, is a purely objective experimental branch of natural science. Its theoretical goal is the prediction and control of behavior. Introspection forms no essential part of its methods, nor is the scientific value of its data dependent upon the readiness with which they lend themselves to interpretation in terms of consciousness.[16]

---

15. William T. Powers. 1995. "The origins of purpose: the first metasystem transitions." *World Futures* 45(1): 125–138. Special issue on The Quantum of Evolution. Available at http://www.livingcontrolsystems.com/intro_papers/evolution_purpose.pdf.

16. John B. Watson. 1913. "Psychology as the Behaviorist Views It." *Psychological Review* 20(2): 158–177.

Behaviorism has deep roots in the worldviews of those who believe actions are responses to environmental stimuli (disturbances) and those who believe that employees are best controlled via carrots and sticks.[17] Behaviorists assert that stimuli are the *input* to the person whose brain and nervous system function to generate an *output* in response. While this view seems logical to many, Powers noted:

> There has, however, always been a nagging problem in the background. William James mentioned it nearly 100 years ago. It is that organisms seem to accomplish repeatable ends by variable means. Taken at face value, this observation means that *there can be no reliable chain connecting antecedent causes to consequent behaviors.* The chain is broken somewhere between the place where muscles contract and the place where we observe the consistent consequences of variable muscle contractions.

> ... Of course, actions are highly variable: they must be, because a natural environment is always disturbing the variables that organisms control. Of course, the consequences of variable actions repeat: they are, or are closely related to, input quantities that organisms are controlling. What we mean by the word *behavior* is not the unpredictable fluctuations of muscle force and limb position that we can see, but the regular consequences that result. We mean controlled variables.[18]

17. Bartley J. Madden. 2014. *Reconstructing Your Worldview: The Four Core Beliefs You Need to Solve Complex Business Problems.* Naperville, IL: LearningWhatWorks.

18. William T. Powers. 1990. "Control theory: a model of organisms." *System Dynamics Review* 6(1): 1–20, pp. 13 and 14; italics added.

In Figure 8, depicting the Behaviorism worldview, the grey arrow shows an Input-Output system that fails to operationalize the role of purpose (reference signal) residing inside the nervous system.[19]

Figure 8:
Behaviorism worldview

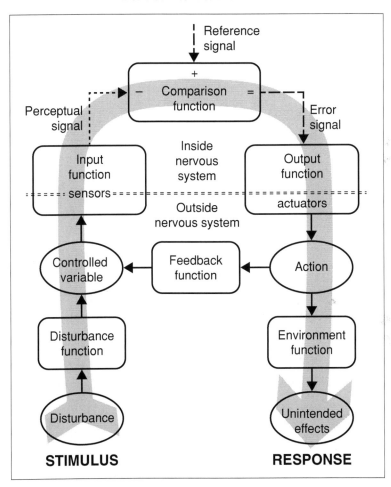

19. William T. Powers. 1973. "Feedback: Beyond Behaviorism." *Science*, 179, No. 4071 pp. 351–356.

With an extreme focus on inputs, the environment is then the prime mover for understanding behavior. To no surprise, B. F. Skinner wrote: "It [Skinner's Behaviorism] offers, I believe, the clearest possible statement of the causal relations between behavior and environment."[20]

#6. What is critically missing from cognitive psychology, which utilizes the findings from cognitive science and is the centerpiece of modern psychology textbooks? In contrast to Behaviorism, with its exclusive focus outside the nervous system, cognitive psychology turned attention to inside the nervous system. As illustrated in Figure 9, processes in the brain became the focus for explaining stimulus and response.[21]

Data from the environment is the input to the brain which instantaneously analyzes the environmental situation, one's goals, and all relevant relationships. The optimum plan of action (output) is computed and commands are sent to the muscles in order to generate the appropriate response. Figure 9 illustrates the widely held assumptions (especially in psychology textbooks) that behavior is the end result of environmental stimuli and cognitive plans.

Notably missing from cognitive psychology is the negative feedback loop mechanism so central to a hierarchical control system that enables actions to control perceptions in a way that is superefficient in achieving one's purposes. Why are control system insights totally missing from psychology textbooks?

---

20. B. F. Skinner. 1974. *About Behaviorism.* New York: Random House, p. 273.

21. Richard S. Marken. 2009. "You Say You Had a Revolution: Methodological Foundations of Closed-Loop Psychology." *Review of General Psychology* 13(2): 137–145.

Figure 9:
Cognitive psychology worldview

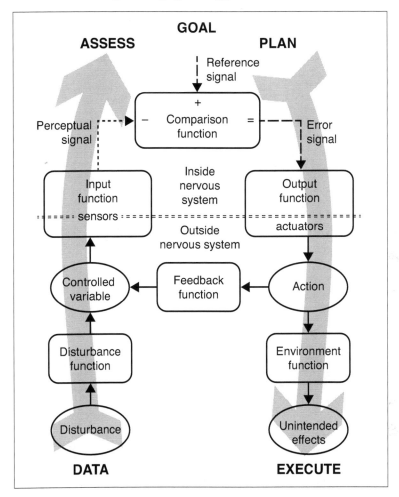

Here is a clue. Changes to textbooks follow highly cited articles in the top journals. Such articles typically bridge gaps in the existing paradigm with theory or empirical contributions. Articles reporting empirical findings typically employ linear cause and effect (stimulus and response) with dependent variables correlated with independent variables, for two reasons. First, doing the research and getting a paper accepted is facilitated. Second, seriously engaging with PCT entails a fundamental break with one's peers, learning a new research methodology, and facing increased difficulties in publishing in the top journals. For sure, this is a huge roadblock for young scholars seeking tenure. And the senior scholars on the editorial boards of the journals control the publication process and have built a legacy of work that supports the existing paradigm. In addition, across the social sciences in general, there is the unspoken expectation that knowledge advancements will be produced by members in good standing in "the club." Club membership almost always requires a PhD and either being a professor or working at a prestigious research facility. Bill Powers was not a member of the club.

Nevertheless, if PCT brings major, *foundational* insights about human behavior, should we not expect that leading thinkers in cognitive science and the philosophy of the mind would eventually appreciate the usefulness of the PCT hierarchical control systems? Bill Powers may never get the recognition he deserves but his ideas may well come to occupy center stage. In the following quote, Andreas K. Engel, Karl J. Friston, and Danica Kragic, leading-edge cognitive scientists by any measure, suggest shifting the direction of mainstream cognitive science so that it is more compatible with PCT:

> The insight that cognition may be fundamentally grounded in action [in contrast to the classical cognitivist approach of making models representing the world] seems to reinforce a radical change in how we conceive of the functional significance of neural patterns. Some argue that brain states prescribe possible actions, rather than describe states of the outside world. Thus, brain states might better be understood as "directives" that guide action, rather than as "representations."[22]

---

22. Andres K. Engel, Karl J. Friston, and Danica Kragic. 2015. *The Pragmatic Turn: Toward Action-Oriented Views in Cognitive Science.* Cambridge, MA: MIT Press, p. 5.

The influential philosopher and cognitive scientist Andy Clark argued for the importance of the brain's ability to predict sensory perceptions and reduce predictive error, which is close to PCT thinking:

> Action is not so much a "response to an input" as a neat and efficient way of selecting the *next* input, driving a rolling cycle ... We thus act so as to bring forth the evolving streams of sensory information that keep us viable ... The largest contributor to ongoing neural response is the ceaseless anticipatory buzz of downwards-flowing neural prediction that *drives perception and action in a circular causal flow.*[23]

The high-powered minds quoted above referenced neither Powers nor PCT, even though PCT seems particularly relevant to their thinking. If they and other leading cognitive scientists used PCT as a foundation to build upon, or at least as a source for hypotheses to be tested, perhaps new useful knowledge could be produced at a faster pace. Alternatively, would we all not benefit from cognitive scientists and particularly the authors of psychology textbooks plainly explaining why they choose to ignore PCT? One can speculate that the answers would represent a defense of linear causation coupled with an input/output experimental mindset and wrapped in a defense of their existing research methodology.

---

23. Andy Clark. 2016. *Surfing Uncertainty: Prediction, Action, and the Embodied Mind.* Oxford: Oxford University Press, p. 52; italics added.

COMPUTATIONAL MODELS, MOTOR SENSORY TRACKING EXPERIMENTS, AND CONTROLLED VARIABLES

As discussed in the above section, PCT and cognitive psychology (the reigning view of human behavior) are radically different. Figure 10 summarizes these differences.

Figure 10:
Two different views of human behavior

PERCEPTUAL CONTROL THEORY	TOPIC	COGNITIVE PSYCHOLOGY
Closed circular loop of causation functions so that what the system does affects what it senses and what it senses affects what it does. Cause and effect happen concurrently.	Time	Linear causation with cause preceding effect
Purpose is center stage and operational-ized as the reduction of error calculated as the difference between the perceptual signal and the reference signal.	Purpose	Recognized but not center stage
People control the consequences of their actions in order to achieve their purposes.	Control	People control their actions to respond to environmental stimuli
Actions feed back to offset disturbances.	Feedback	Ignored
Controlled variable changes little even when encountering continual disturbances.	Controlled variable	Ignored
Research would benefit from the use of a hierarchy-of-control-systems structure.	Brain and nervous system	Large-scale research in progress (e.g., neu-roscience)

As noted in Figure 10, cognitive psychology ignores feedback and the controlled variable so prominent in Perceptual Control Theory. The key points noted in this figure constitute a potential paradigm change for understanding human behavior. Consider the last point about the brain and nervous system. Cognitive psychology employs an input/output mindset in which the brain (treated as a supercomputer) *receives inputs* about the environment and optimizes output (action). In contrast, the PCT mindset emphasizes how the *individual person chooses inputs*, i.e., what is important to them (controlled variables and reference states). The criticism that PCT is analogous to controlling a machine and ill-suited to human behavior is misinformed and reflects a lack of knowledge about PCT.

Tracking experiments, discussed below, are powerful tools in explaining how PCT works. However, those not entirely familiar with PCT will need some further "big picture" insights in order to be motivated to read articles about tracking experiments and/ or using their own computer to participate in one or more tracking experiments.[24] They need to feel comfortable in replacing (at least, provisionally) the belief that we control our actions with the idea that we control the consequences of our actions.

We walk without falling down, safely drive a car, brew a pot of coffee, drink a cup of coffee, and perform endless other tasks using variable actions that yield the same outcome. How so? This is explained by viewing behavior as control of perceptions such as your foot touching the ground in a way that maintains balance; the position of your car in its lane; the temperature, color, and taste of the brewed coffee; and adjustments in raising the coffee cup to your lips as the weight diminishes due to less liquid in the cup. Does it not make sense that you control the consequences of your actions such as the perception of the coffee cup touching your lips?

Adopt this PCT mindset and see where it takes you. The first step is to realize that observing what people do can easily lead to a superficial understanding of their behavior. Understanding flows from discovering controlled variables important to the person and then observing how their actions are attempts to keep their controlled variables where they want them to be.

---

24. See these websites: The International Association for Perceptual Control Theory at iapct.org, PCTweb.org, LivingControlSystems.com, and especially MindReadings. com for tracking demonstrations in which you can control the cursor and react to disturbances.

Say you observe drivers who stop at a gas station and you further observe that, on average, the amount of money spent indicates a low amount of gas in the tank when they entered the station. You conclude that behavior in this situation is clearly understood. Not really. PCT is about explaining the behavior of an individual person, not averages or central tendencies of people. A person with the same low amount of gas left in the tank may drive by this gas station when she is controlling for being on time for an important meeting. Controlled variables can be difficult to pinpoint. Was it more important to that particular driver who stopped at the gas station to get gasoline or to get a caffeine fix by buying a cup of coffee?

PCT views the person as doing the controlling and not mechanistically responding to environmental stimuli such as the gas gauge indicating one quarter full. A husband may fill up the tank in his wife's car when the gauge reads half full. In this instance, he is controlling for his wife's feelings since she appreciates the help in avoiding a future visit to the gas station.

You may push back and say: "Look at that driver's gas gauge which is almost empty. Clearly, I *know* what caused him to pull into the gas station because I can *see* the almost empty gas gauge." Seeing an environmental stimulus coupled to a response gives us a false sense of certainty as to understanding behavior. A deeper analysis reveals that the controlled variable is safety. He is controlling for safety on the road, and avoiding an empty tank is a way to control for safety. Moreover, on another occasion he may stop at the gas station with plenty of gas in his tank. In this instance, he feels that one of his tires may be experiencing a slow leak, and checking air pressure in the tire controls for safety—a different action to keep a controlled variable (safety) where he wants it. We control the consequences of our actions. The first step in understanding behavior is to discover a person's controlled variables relevant to the situation at hand.

We tend to be on automatic pilot every day in implicitly assigning cause to an environmental stimulus that is followed by a response (action). Keep in mind that this common experience of analyzing behavior begins with observing the stimulus and correlated action. *We almost never begin with a person's controlled variables, which often can be difficult to discover.* As previously noted, Powers labeled this noncritical and superficial way of observing what people do in apparent response to a stimulus as a behavioral illusion.[25]

PCT like any theory needs to be tested to observe if its predictions are verified and if it helps us understand what is really happening. A reasonable initial test would focus on motor sensory tasks in which the disturbances and actions are visible and quantifiable. The motor sensory experiments have provided the strongest support for the PCT explanation of human behavior and are definitely worth your time to personally experience.

The basic idea behind a computational (software coded) model is straightforward. For example, a motor sensory task is studied and, based on PCT principles (or whatever theory the researcher relies on to explain human behavior), a model is constructed in precise mathematical terms and converted into computer code.[26] The mathematical precision of a computational model overcomes the lack of specificity in verbal theories that are open to myriad interpretations. The model can be run and the simulated

25. Richard S. Marken. 1992. *Mind Readings: Experimental Studies of Purpose.* Durango, CO: A Control Systems Group Book, Chapter 1.

26. Richard S. Marken authored three useful books on PCT models: 1992. *Mind Readings: Experimental Studies of Purpose.* A Control Systems Group Book; 2002. *More Mind Readings: Methods and Models in the Study of Purpose.* St. Louis, MO: New View; and 2014. *Doing Research on Purpose.* St. Louis, MO: New View. Also useful are two books of selected papers (relevant to modeling) by Bill Powers compiled by the Control Systems Group, Inc., Gravel Switch, Kentucky: *Living Control Systems* and *Living Control Systems II.* And for advanced modeling, see William T. Powers. 2008. *Living Control Systems III: The Fact of Control.* Bloomfield, NJ: Benchmark Publications.

results compared to actual behavioral results. Significant differences call for developing a more refined (complex) model. And the process continues, all the while the researcher is learning more about how people are actually controlling their lives. Powers commented about computational models:

> In contrast to the method of statistical generalization, the method of modeling begins by analyzing an individual behaving system. First, the system is broken down into actual or proposed components, each of which can be described as a simple input-output relationship. Then the equations describing each component are solved as a simultaneous system to predict the individual's behavior, given the actions of any independent outside influences. The calculated behavior is compared against the actual behavior with those same influences acting. The difference between the model's behavior and the real behavior provides a basis for systematically revising the hypothetical components of the model (the known components, of course, remain the same) until its calculated behavior is in accord with observation. The method of modeling is the basis for most procedures in the physical sciences. Generalizations come afterward, not first. There is, in fact, almost no use of statistical generalization in the most successful sciences. The focus is on constructing and improving models.[27]

Tracking experiments involve building and debugging a PCT-based computer model, running simulations, and analyzing the output. This output is then compared to the output generated by

---

27. William T. Powers. 1990. "Control Theory and Statistical Generalizations." *American Behavioral Scientist* 34(1): 24–31. In this article Powers presents a brief but highly revealing demonstration of how multiple regression can lead to wrong conclusions about economic behavior. *Every economist—actually everyone who uses multiple regression—would benefit from studying Powers' way of thinking so elegantly laid out in these eight pages.*

human subjects under the identical conditions as used for the simulations. Depending upon the behavior being investigated, PCT tracking models can become increasingly complex to address the complexity of the underlying system being studied.

The simplest motor sensory tracking experiments involve a subject looking at a computer screen with an ability to move a mouse in order to position the cursor in line with a designated target. A simulation is run in which the computer generates a continual stream of random disturbances over time that move the cursor away from the designated target. This information is available to the model and, in turn, actions are generated exactly as specified by the model.

The output of the tracking simulation is a plotted time series of the disturbances (movement away from the target), actions taken (movement of the cursor), and the extent of control achieved, i.e., how close over time the cursor stays to the target. As highlighted in Figure 11, there are three especially important questions to answer.

A large number of tracking experiments of varying complexity have generated simulations showing that the PCT model generates a system under control.[28] The outputs show that actions instantaneously offset disturbances, and the controlled variable changes very little over time, thereby maintaining the desired perception (zero error). The simulation results are impressive. But, critically important is the answer to this question: do the actions generated by the model match the actions taken by human subjects? Yes, they do. Consequently, these tracking

28. Warren Mansell and Vyv Huddy. 2018. "The Assessment and Modeling of Perceptual Control: A Transformation in Research Methodology to Address the Replication Crisis." *Review of General Psychology* 22(3): 305–320. Also see Maximilian G. Parker, Andrew B. S. Willett, Sarah F. Tyson, Andrew P. Weightman, and Warren Mansell. "A Systematic Evaluation of the Evidence for Perceptual Control Theory in Tracking Studies." *Neuroscience and Biobehavioral Reviews.* 112 (May 2020): 616–633.

experiments support the PCT view that we humans function with a brain and nervous system that operate via the negative feedback loop principle. It is difficult to argue that one can understand what is happening in these tracking experiments by ignoring negative feedback control.

Figure 11:
Three important questions

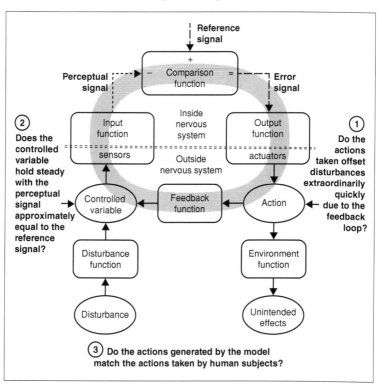

As more complex behavior is studied, an iterative process ensues. A computational model is built and tested with both simulated results and actual behavior. This typically reveals a deficiency in the original model, motivating the researcher to build a more complex model to better duplicate actual behavior. For example, programming in DOS in the early 1990s, Bill Powers successfully built and tested a model of the functioning of a human arm and hand, which was published in a Windows version in his last book. He used a hierarchical multiple-leveled system with multiple negative feedback control systems at each level.[29]

Let's consider the process for discovering a controlled variable. Your initial hunch that one or more controlled variables are active in the operation of a system typically is due to a system's unexpected steadiness (lack of variation). The Test for the Controlled Variable (TCV) begins with a guess about what perceptual variable the system is sensing and controlling. This guess or hypothesis can be informed by assessing the purposeful goals of the system. The next step is to apply disturbances that should have an observable effect on the variable in question if it is not under control. Consider the earlier example of my wife playing the TV in a room adjacent to my office. If my office door is opened and then I immediately close this door to offset the noise disturbance, that is evidence of the discovery of a controlled variable. Creativity and perseverance are helpful for implementing the TCV.

A research program addressed the question of the identification of a controlled variable for beavers that had constructed a dam.[30] The hypothesis was that a controlled variable was the noise level of running water. To implement the TCV, the researchers placed a loudspeaker near the dam that played the sound of running water. To counteract the noise disturbance, the beavers piled mud on the speaker indicating that a controlled variable was discovered.

In dealing with more complex systems than a beaver dam, PCT researchers discover controlled variables by an iterative process of assuming a particular perceptual variable is controlled, building a model, and comparing the simulation results to actual

---

29. William T. Powers. 2008. *Living Control Systems III: The Fact of Control.* Bloomfield, NJ: Benchmark Publications, Chapter 8.

30. P. B. Richard. 1983. "Mechanisms and adaptation in the constructive behavior of the beaver (*C. fiber L.*)." *Acta Zoologica Fennica* 174, 105–108.

behavior. Consequently, a learning process unfolds as to how the system functions and which variables are controlled.[31]

The next section addresses PCT's hierarchy of control systems that enable a person to have multiple controlled variables, at different hierarchical levels, operating simultaneously.

PCT HIERARCHY OF CONTROL SYSTEMS

Powers proposed a nested hierarchy of control systems with eleven levels, or classes of perceptions, as enumerated in Figure 12. This figure is simplified to illustrate the conceptual functioning of such a hierarchy.[32] The basic unit of analysis is a control system with a negative feedback loop, as previously discussed. Referring to the bottom of Figure 12, the input (I) function converts physical variables to a neural perceptual (P) signal that is compared to the reference (R) signal in the comparison (C) function. The resulting error (E) signal is converted to muscle movements in the output (O) function. The controlled variable (CV) is impacted by the disturbance (D) and an offsetting action (A).

The above hierarchy solves a fundamental problem: in a continually changing world, we can't preplan the actions needed to maintain control. The solution is variable actions that yield repeatable consequences. Being in control means that actions are quickly taken to offset disturbances in order to keep the perception of a controlled variable equal to the reference signal (intended

31. William T. Powers, Bruce Abbott, Timothy A. Carey, David M. Goldstein, Warren Mansell, Richard S. Marken, Bruce Nevin, Richard Robertson, and Martin Taylor. "Perceptual Control Theory: A Model for Understanding the Mechanisms and Phenomena of Control," in Dag Forssell (ed.). 2016. *Perceptual Control Theory: An Overview of the Third Grand Theory in Psychology Introductions, Readings, and Resources*. Hayward, CA: Living Control Systems Publishing, pages 32–33 offer a concise and useful mathematical summary of PCT.

32. Adapted from Shelley Roy. 2008. *A People Primer: The Nature of Living Systems*. Chapel Hill, NC: New View Publications. This is a useful nontechnical explanation of PCT, as is William T. Powers. 1998. *Making Sense of Behavior: The Meaning of Control*. New Canaan, CT: Benchmark Publications.

perception—what we want to experience) sent from a higher level in the hierarchy. Note that what you *experience* (see, hear, smell, etc.) is generated by neural signals in your brain. Many internal neural signals at different perceptual levels represent the complex attributes of what we perceive in the external world.

Figure 12:
PCT's hierarchy of control systems

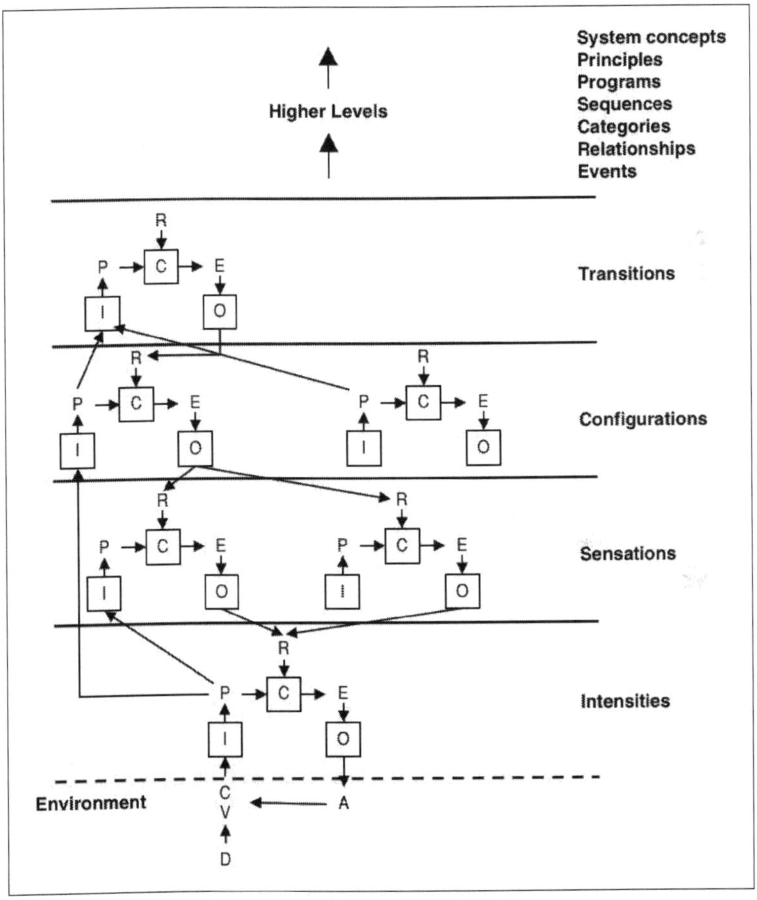

Importantly, the PCT hierarchy differs from a command-and-control hierarchy that specifies actions to be taken. With the PCT hierarchy, higher levels do not issue commands for action; rather, they tell lower-level systems what to perceive. For example, walking along the sidewalk you fail to notice the "wet cement" sign and step where you shouldn't have. With a slow-moving command-and-control hierarchy that needs to both compute and communicate a new plan of action, expect to very soon be face down in cement. With PCT, the foot position control system receives a smoothly varying reference signal from the next higher level (see Figure 12). With your foot suddenly stuck in wet cement, the foot position system experiences a big error signal, resulting in a powerful action that quickly pulls your foot out of the cement and restores your balance. Lower-level systems operate considerably faster than higher level systems.

Returning to Figure 12, let's discuss the logic of Powers' proposed eleven levels, or classes of perception. As he noted, these levels are not etched in stone; rather, consider accepting them provisionally by recognizing that future research may lead to modification.

Ascending the levels illustrated in Figure 12 answers the question why lower levels have particular reference signals (purposes) while descending the levels answers the question how higher-level purposes are achieved. At the lowest level, *intensities* indicate what is happening to nerve endings and report the degree (quantity) of stimulation acting on them. *Sensations* (e.g., brightness, pressure, temperature, etc.) enable objects to be distinguished from one another. Next up are *configurations* that represent particular sensations which constitute a shape being recognized as a unit.

In moving up to a higher level, keep in mind that the control of perceptions at a particular level depends on being able to vary lower-level perceptions. So, what higher level perceptions can be controlled via intensities, sensations, and configurations? A plausible answer is the experience of change. We experience change in the world, and therefore *transitions* (going from a perception of cold to warm when entering a house during a frigid winter) are the next logical higher level.

A reasonable next level is *events* which are packages of perceptions that follow a pattern (saying hello, shaking a friend's hand, etc.). *Relationships* tie together a bark with a dog and a meow with a cat. *Categories* reflect either-or classifications that differentiate things (a horse not a cow, a motorcycle not a bicycle, etc.). *Sequences* represent perceptions that follow a specified order. After your income tax return is completed, you write a check to cover what is owed, and then mail these items to the Internal Revenue Service.

Programs connect sequences due to specific choices; for example, if X do Y and if not X do Z. Control of a perception of a program depends on handling lower-level perceptions to comport with the logic and rational thinking reflected in the program. *Principles* are difficult to precisely define and are about ways of living one's life as, for example, an honest person, a reliable employee, and the like. *System concepts* are about big organizing ideas such as a firm's mission statement, capitalism, democracy, religious beliefs, etc. Finally, starting at the highest level, as one moves down, there are more loops that act faster and the levels become more concrete.

An especially rich vein of research involves generating additional insights about the role of memory in setting reference signals and about the role of the PCT hierarchy as part of learning. Also, how might a hierarchy of control systems facilitate imagination and the generation of hypotheses for solving problems?[33]

---

33. Step 5 in Figure 1 focuses on using imagination to develop novel connections that can lead to significant innovations. My upcoming work on this topic will give close attention to the following: Ann M. Pendleton-Jullian and John Seely Brown. 2018. *Design Unbound: Designing for Emergence in a White Water World*. Volumes 1 and 2. Cambridge, MA: MIT Press. On page 397 of Volume 2, the authors state: "... one understands *what is* by using the imagination to generate possibilities of *what could be*. Every thing and experience is understood from two temporal perspectives—both what it actually is in the here and now, and the possibilities the imagination allows us to see in it. And this is a way of being in the world, as well as a way of learning about the world."

Interestingly, considerable empirical support exists for the emergence of a hierarchy of different levels of perception in infants based on the number of weeks since birth. With infants, the gaining of a new perceptual level is marked by a temporary regression of capabilities and anxiety (crankiness). Reorganization (a form of learning) of their control systems occurs with trial-and-error experimentation until increased control is achieved with their new capabilities. Hetty van de Rijt and Frans Plooij—coauthors of *The Wonder Weeks*, a widely read guidebook for parents of newborn infants—first observed the distinct regularity (as to the number of weeks since birth) of regression periods followed by leaps in cognitive development from extensive observational studies of free-living chimpanzee babies. They later learned that their observations agreed with Powers' hierarchy of perceptual levels. Decades of research followed, focusing on human babies and their relationships with their mothers and replicating the chimpanzee baby findings. Their subsequent PCT-oriented studies are relevant to the evolution of human cognition.[34]

Powers thought that the PCT hierarchy of perceptual levels holds potential for handling conflict. Timothy Carey built on this idea and developed the Method of Levels (MOL) for psychotherapy.[35] Conflict occurs when two control systems at one level of the hierarchy are sending opposing reference signals to the same lower level, which explains how chronic psychological distress occurs. The greater the degree of control, the more intense the conflict. Conflicts endure due to a person continually struggling with incompatible actions. The PCT-guided solution is for the MOL therapist to engage the patient in conversations and shift aware-

34. Mikael Heimann (ed.). 2003. *Regression Periods in Human Infancy.* Mahwah, NJ: Erlbaum.

35. Timothy A. Carey. 2006. *The Method of Levels: How to Do Psychotherapy Without Getting in the Way.* Hayward, CA: Living Control Systems Publishing. See Carey's website MethodofLevels.com.au.

ness to the level at which the conflict originates. This can lead to an *aha!* moment for patients when they plainly see the root cause of their difficulties.

MOL is grounded in the solid science of PCT and brings a needed focus to psychotherapy, which unfortunately is populated by a wide range of practices missing a solid scientific basis. Psychology textbooks and popular books are replete with arbitrary classification schemes absent a unifying theory about why we act in the ways we do.

Warren Mansell, Timothy Carey, and Sara Tai summarize:

> Control could well be a unifying phenomenon for the life sciences. It is certainly crucial when it comes to understanding and treating psychological problems ... problems of living are, fundamentally, problems of control ... from the perspective of control, we might achieve greater clarity and resolution of some of the most contentious theoretical issues in psychology ... [including] the debate about common versus specific factors, the 'dodo bird hypothesis' (the idea that all psychotherapy is equally effective), the categorization of problems into apparently discrete disorders, the mind/body split, the interaction between the environment and the individual's goals, and the divide between psychological and physical problems. Ultimately, we might provide treatments that are more effective and more efficient because they will be based on a more accurate depiction of why we act in the ways we do.[36]

The above quote speaks volumes about PCT's potential to serve as a unifying theory in the social sciences. PCT mathematics enable

---

36. Warren Mansell, Timothy A. Carey, and Sara Tai. 2013. *A Transdiagnostic Approach to CBT Using Method of Levels Therapy.* London: Routledge, p. 20.

precise language to expedite scientific progress.[37] Would not progress accelerate by shifting from an *external* observer viewpoint to the *internal* control processes that generate the observed actions in order to maintain perceptions at desired states? PCT-oriented research raises fertile questions for scientists about how our brains function and suggests possible tie-ins to closed-loop causation and negative feedback loops.[38] However, empirical research in psychology correlates both independent and dependent variables and often seems designed to eliminate any role for feedback. Since important controlled variables are notable due to their absence of change, how can psychologists, *under the existing linear cause-and-effect paradigm*, investigate controlled variables that exhibit a lack of correlation to other environmental variables?

PCT FOR BUSINESS FIRMS

A PCT mindset holds promise for new angles of thinking for academics conducting management research. The thinking undergirding the Method of Levels can assist management and their HR (human resource) departments in spending less time measuring the effectiveness of their carrots-and-sticks initiatives and more time analyzing employees' controlled variables/hierarchical levels as this relates to reducing conflicts and increasing

---

37. The mathematics of PCT control systems impress for elegance and practicality. On this topic, a particularly informative book will be published by Cambridge University Press in early 2021: *The Study of Living Control Systems*, by Richard S. Marken.

38. Important neuroscience research on the basal ganglia provides insights about basic motor functioning of human beings. See Henry H. Yin. 2017. "The basal ganglia in action." *Neuroscientist* 23(3): 299–313. Yin employed a PCT hierarchical model. He describes the need for a PCT methodology that puts control with inputs not outputs: "The key mistake is to assume that a control system controls its outputs, the convention taught in engineering ... the controlled variable is not the output but the input. Biological organisms are autonomous, which means that they possess intrinsic reference signals, whether innate or learned ... The control of output assumption reverses the organism/environment relationship. Consequently, attempts to apply control theory to neuroscience have largely failed, even though the correct equations were used. It is as if one were to use the wrong end of a key to open a lock, only to conclude that it was the wrong key."

cooperation. The PCT explanation of human behavior could advance both research methodology and the generation of novel hypotheses to spur imagination by overcoming an automatic reliance on correlations of dependent variables with independent variables.

In reporting on their extensive research into employee motivation, Teresa Amabile and Steven Kramer note the following (PCT tie-ins are shown as bracketed and italicized words):

> Conventional management wisdom is way off track about employee psychology [*understanding human behavior*]. When we surveyed hundreds of managers around the world, ranging from CEOs to project leaders, about what motivates employees, we found startling results: 95 percent of these leaders fundamentally misunderstood the most important source of motivation. Our research inside companies revealed that the best way to motivate people, day in and day out, is by facilitating *progress*—even small wins. But the managers in our survey ranked "supporting progress" dead last.
>
> ... When you do what it takes to facilitate progress in work people care about [*controlled variable*], managing them—and managing the organization—becomes much more straightforward. You don't need to parse people's psyches or tinker with their incentives, because helping them succeed at making a difference virtually guarantees good inner work life *and* strong performance.[39]

Consider the Theory of Jobs to be Done developed over a 20-year period by Clayton Christensen and his colleagues. Christensen argues that understanding customers does not drive innovation

---

39. Teresa Amabile and Steven Kramer. 2011. *The Progress Principle: Using Small Wins to Ignite Joy, Engagement, and Creativity at Work*. Boston: Harvard Business Review Press, pp. 3 and 10.

success. Rather, understanding customer jobs does. In a nut-shell, here are the key elements:

> Part of the problem is that we're missing the right vocab-ulary to talk about innovation in ways that help us understand what actually *causes* it to succeed ... This involves creating the right set of *experiences* that accom-pany your product or service in solving the job ... We define a "job" as the *progress that a person is trying to make in a particular circumstance.*[40]

In the above quote, Christensen and his coauthors italicized cer-tain words for emphasis. Are they not focusing on the PCT logic of controlled variables that are important to customers in achiev-ing a goal (job to be done)? They conclude that the conventional correlation studies focused on consumer preferences are incon-sequential. Such a conclusion should warm the hearts of PCT proponents.

The coauthors of the initial *Harvard Business Review* article that introduced the Jobs Theory included Christensen and Scott Cook, cofounder of Intuit and an early adopter of the Jobs Theory.[41] Cook's Intuit team developed an innovative accounting software product, QuickBooks. They focused not on duplicating the func-tionality of their competitors' products but on what mattered most in getting the job done that customers needed done. Impor-tantly, that put the spotlight on the controlled variable for mini-mizing the customer's time in learning the language and rules used in the accounting profession.

---

40. Clayton M. Christensen, Taddy Hall, Karen Dillon, and David S. Duncan. 2016. *Competing Against Luck: The Story of Innovation and Customer Choice.* New York: Harper Business, pp. 14, 16, and 27; italics in original.

41. Clayton Christensen, Scott Cook, and Taddy Hall. 2005. "Marketing Malprac-tice: The Cause and the Cure." *Harvard Business Review,* December 83(12): 74–83.

... QuickBooks might have seemed an unlikely success. After all, the product offered *half* the functionality of more sophisticated accounting software at *twice* the price. But QuickBooks quickly became—and has remained—the global leader in online accounting software. Competitors were focused on making the best *accounting* software possible. Cook and his team focused on the job customers were trying to do.[42]

Consider the common situation of a command-and-control management organization that is short-term focused to the detriment of long-term value creation and all of the firm's stakeholders. Carrots and sticks replace an appreciation for what deeply matters to employees (their controlled variables). Managers' skill is not in mentoring employees to improve their problem-solving skills but in firefighting and workarounds as part of doing whatever it takes to meet short-term accounting targets. This carrots-and-sticks approach to managing people represents a linear causation mindset that would put a smile on the face of John B. Watson, who pioneered behaviorism. In contrast, it would put a frown on the face of Peter Drucker, who, some 50 years ago, wrote about the knowledge worker: "... no one can motivate him. He has to motivate himself. No one can direct him. He has to direct himself ... He is the guardian of his own standards, of his own performance, and of his own objectives."[43]

How might PCT principles be revealed in a long-term-value-creating firm that contravenes the short-term-command-and-control firm? What quickly comes to mind is Lean Thinking, which optimizes the flow of products and services via value streams that encompass the entire production process. Skilled

42. Clayton M. Christensen, Taddy Hall, Karen Dillon, and David S. Duncan. 2016. *Competing Against Luck: The Story of Innovation and Customer Choice*. New York: HarperBusiness, p. 63.

43. Peter F. Drucker. 1973. *Management: Tasks, Responsibilities, Practices*. New York: HarperBusiness, p. 279.

lean practitioners have a worldview decidedly different from one focused on using any means necessary to hit accounting targets. Lean thinking, as practiced by preeminent firms like Toyota and Danaher, entails a knowledge-building culture that continually purges waste (including time) throughout a product's value stream. Lean employees, guided by manager mentors, learn by solving problems as part of a cognitive process that Toyota calls *kata*. It is a pattern of thinking and behaving consistent with both value creation and a win-win partnership between employees and management. Mike Rother, a leading expert on these topics, offers this description:

> Toyota's improvement kata involves teaching people a standardized conscious "means" for sensing the gist of situations and responding scientifically. This is a different way for humans to have a sense of *security, comfort, and confidence.* Instead of obtaining that from an unrealistic sense of certainty about conditions, they get it from the means by which they deal with uncertainty. This channels and taps our capabilities as humans much better than our current management approach, explains a good deal of Toyota's success, and gives us a model for managing almost any human enterprise.[44]

The above italicized words "security, comfort, and confidence" are emblematic of a working experience that is highly desirable for employees—controlled variables that are critical for job satisfaction and productivity.

Another application of the PCT mindset is to fill a gap in the organizational change literature. Often *systems thinking* is used to analyze a firm's organizational structure and culture (how things are done). And, as part of a proposed change program, employees are put into categories that seem plausible, e.g., old school and

44. Mike Rother. 2010. *Toyota Kata: Managing People for Improvement, Adaptiveness, and Superior Results.* New York: McGraw Hill, p. 165; italics added.

difficult to move in a new direction. However, each employee is an autonomous living *control system*, and their controlled variables, reference states, and high-level goals hold the key to gaining support for the change program. A PCT approach connects systems thinking down to the goals of individual employees.

INDUSTRIAL ORGANIZATION (I-O)

The academic discipline of industrial organization (I-O) is keenly interested in employee motivation in business firms and related topics. The path of control theory in general, and PCT in particular, in gaining recognition in I-O has been succinctly analyzed by Jeffrey Vancouver in Chapter 12 of the *Interdisciplinary Handbook of Perceptual Control Theory*, which is a magisterial compilation of insights from many leading PCT researchers. In the remaining part of this section, I'll highlight Vancouver's analysis.

Powers' 1973 book, *Behavior: The Control of Perception*, which rigorously and comprehensively introduced PCT, encountered an I-O research environment that favored qualitative, system-level, verbal theories. In contrast, PCT explained the behavior of subsystems (people) and facilitated quantitative computational models. This gap has been narrowed in recent years as more I-O researchers appreciate how PCT explains so much so parsimoniously.

In the early 1980s, I-O's emphasis on motivation was expanded to address how the setting of goals affected employee performance. PCT made inroads by investigating how feedback could influence performance. Research articles expanded control theory, although frequently not following the conceptual details described by Powers.[45]

---

45. Powers considered non-PCT control systems as the "analyze-compute-act" model which requires a beyond-belief knowledge and computational speed to handle control problems of practical interest.

According to Vancouver, the 1990s began with growing academic resistance to PCT. However, that was gradually countered by empirical work that tied control theory to the favored I-O issues of goal setting, motivation, feedback, job satisfaction, and self-efficacy (belief in one's ability to achieve a performance goal). To no surprise, those in the trenches doing empirical work became more cognizant of the high degree of difficulty in transitioning from their linear correlation studies to PCT empirical studies. Vancouver summarizes the state of affairs for control theory (not necessarily PCT) and I-O at the end of the 20th century:

> ... the theorizing was verbal ... conceptual arguments ... were not represented computationally or mathematically to determine if they were internally consistent ... researchers were not cognizant of the methodological requirements for examining control theory propositions ... although most realized that control theory was dynamic and that data therefore needed to be controlled longitudinally, they lacked a full appreciation of the difficulties involved in studying dynamic processes.[46]

So far in the 21st century, I-O researchers are increasingly aware of the payoff from connecting the micro subsystems explained by control theory to the macro systems level concerned with decision making. My sense is that CEOs and other managers would make better decisions (especially human resource related) if they were well versed in PCT.

Since 2000, empirical work in I-O related to control theory significantly expanded (often in combination with other theories). Keep in mind that PCT testing in business environments is

---

46. Jeffrey B. Vancouver. 2020. "Perceptions of control theory in industrial-organizational psychology: disturbances and counter-disturbances." in Warren Mansell (ed.) *The Interdisciplinary Handbook of Perceptual Control Theory: Living Control Systems IV.* London: Academic Press, p. 474.

decidedly more difficult compared to the motor sensory tracking experiments previously discussed.

To sum up, management researchers (and other social science researchers) face a monumentally important choice concerning a research paradigm. If they embrace the PCT mindset, they would organize their research based on the belief that behavior is the control of perception and perception deserves to be the fundamental unit of analysis.[47] If they are decidedly more comfortable with either behaviorism or cognitive psychology, they are choosing a belief that behavior is about actions in response to external stimuli.[48]

CONCLUDING THOUGHTS

Perceptual Control Theory has a remarkably wide range of potential applications, including any discipline that involves the study of human behavior (most certainly psychology), research on the brain and nervous system, and research on technology that mimics human behavior (AI, robotic systems). Even more broadly, PCT can serve as a basis for communication about, and understanding of, the behavior of all living organisms. Innovative work on the hierarchical organization of behavior for perception-based robotics is ongoing.[49] Machine learning for face recognition is tying higher-level perceptions

---

47. For a tutorial on how to create and test computational models see Jeffrey B. Vancouver and Justin M. Weinhardt. 2012. "Modeling the Mind and the Milieu: Computational Modeling for Micro-Level Organizational Researchers." *Organizational Research Methods* 15(4): 602–623. See also Justin M. Weinhardt and Jeffrey B. Vancouver. 2012. "Computational models and organizational psychology: Opportunities abound." *Organizational Psychology Review* 2(4): 267–292.

48. For an insightful rebuttal to a variety of PCT criticisms, see Martin Taylor. 1999. "Editorial: Perceptual Control Theory and its application." *International Journal of Human-Computer Studies* 50(6): 433–444.

49. See the website perceptualrobots.com, which summarizes Rupert Young's research. See also the research publications of Professor Roger K. Moore at the University of Sheffield.

to lower-level perceptions.[50] However, search the neuroscience literature for PCT-driven research and you will likely be disappointed, although there are researchers who march to the beat of a different drummer, such as Henry Yin, professor of psychology and neuroscience at Duke University. Yin is a rare combination of being highly skilled in both neuroscience and PCT. He summarizes the current mindset in psychology and neuroscience:

> The dominant paradigm in the study of behavior today is the *linear causation paradigm*. This paradigm, inspired by classical physics, assumes that causes precede effects, that the behavior of organisms is caused by antecedent events inside and outside the organism, and that future states such as goals and purposes cannot possibly cause behavior. *It is the basis of the general linear model in psychology and the input/output analysis in neuroscience.* But linear causation does not apply to any control system with negative feedback ... Rather than the effect of some prior cause, behavior is the observable manifestation of control in teleological systems that act on the environment to make inputs match their internal reference states.[51]

In addition, Erling O. Jorgensen has described innovative ways to blend PCT and neuroscience:

> ... the functional template of PCT components has a very diverse means of enactment in the nervous system. The brain is an exceedingly complicated set of structures.

50. Hinglak Lee, Roger Grosse, Rajesh Ranganath, and Andrew Y. Ng. 2009. "Convolutional Deep Belief Networks for Scalable Unsupervised Learning of Hierarchical Representations." *Proceedings of the 26th International Conference on Machine Learning*.

51. Henry H. Yin. 2013. "Restoring Purpose in Behavior." In Gianluca Baldassarre and Marco Mirolli (eds.) *Computational and Robotic Models of the Hierarchical Organization of Behavior*. New York: Springer, p. 319; italics added.

And yet, overlaying a set of neurophysiological maps with the engineering blueprint proposed by Perceptual Control Theory offers a promising way to explore the brain's many twists and turns.[52]

Let's focus on language. Bruce Nevin has used PCT for initiating a research program to understand how we learn and use language to benefit ourselves and others, and especially how we control language perceptions. Interestingly, Nevin points out that the stages in which children learn language correlate with the stages of development (previously discussed) during which children operationalize the eleven perceptual levels.

Those working in organizations concerned with improving system performance use language to communicate and gain support for proposed changes to improve performance. And the operation of that changed system involves employees using language. Surely, foundational research about language and behavior represents another rich vein with the potential to gain insights applicable to improving the productivity of systems that involve people. This research differs from the linear cause-and-effect research in the hard sciences. Nevin emphasizes this point:

> The physical sciences *must* construct abstract mathematical models because the Reality which they represent is inaccessible to direct perception. But the subject matter of PCT and of linguistics consists only of perceptions ... the Test for the Controlled Variable explicitly establishes intersubjective agreement between the investigator and the subject organism ... Because language is entirely a product of intersubjective agreement,

---

52. Erling O. Jorgensen in Warren Mansell (ed.). 2020. *The Interdisciplinary Handbook of Perceptual Control Theory.* London: Academic Press, p. 191.

the science of language has a claim on objectivity that it is more immediate than that of any other science.[53]

Kent McClelland sees PCT providing an improved research methodology to gain insights about key issues in sociology:

I have turned to agent-based computational modeling because of several advantages ... its inherent dynamism, its simultaneous focus on micro interactions and emergent macro patterns, its greater realism at the micro level, and its enhanced degree of scientific rigorousness ... this agent-based computational [PCT] model, which re-conceptualizes conflict as a struggle for control, goes beyond conventional theoretical approaches and offers new possibilities of scientific advancement in the sociological study of the time dynamics of conflict.[54]

As a *foundational* understanding of human behavior, PCT offers significant opportunities for more productive living in general, and in particular for the adoption of a new paradigm to improve research and education in the social sciences.[55] For example, consider the topic of improving a person's skill in doing certain tasks, which certainly has enormous importance, ranging from patient rehabilitation to productivity gains in businesses and organizations of all kinds. The PCT view is that human action serves to control perception. Rather than instructions about

53. Bruce Nevin. "Language and thought as control of perception." In Warren Mansell (ed.). 2020. *The Interdisciplinary Handbook of Perceptual Control Theory.* London: Academic Press, p. 445; italics in original.

54. Kent McClelland. 2014. "Cycles of Conflict: A Computational Modeling Alternative to Collins's Theory of Conflict Escalation." *Sociological Theory* 32(2): 100–127.

55. Warren Mansell. 2020. "Ten vital elements of perceptual control theory, tracing the pathway from implicit influence to scientific advance." In Warren Mansell (ed.) *The Interdisciplinary Handbook of Perceptual Control Theory.* London: Academic Press, Chapter 16.

observable actions, could performance be more enhanced via instructions about desired perceptions? Preliminary research says yes.[56] Perceptual Control Theory offers a truly wide span of opportunities.

Included in this opportunity set is economics, which is concerned with tradeoffs, incentives, choices, and model building. Much empirical research in economics uses multiple regression that imposes (linear) open-loop causation on human behavior. This is contrary to the closed-loop causation keyed to negative feedback loops that has explained how human subjects behave in motor sensory tracking experiments. Would not economists, and their students, benefit from working with Perceptual Control Theory that explains so much about human behavior in a concise and precise language that should especially appeal to economic theorists?

Let's return to how business firms may benefit from PCT. The beginning point is a strategy for PCT adoption in the business world that is focused on an important controlled variable of hard-nosed managers—the perception of system improvement at all levels of the firm. Figure 1 details seven steps to improve performance. Regarding Step 1, a strong case has been presented that PCT provides clarity as to why people behave as they do and deserves to be one's foundational explanation of human behavior.

A sensible strategy is to position the understanding and application of PCT as the *necessary first step in improving system performance.*

---

56. Carla Brown-Ojeda and Warren Mansell. 2018. "Do Perceptual Instructions Lead to Enhanced Performance Relative to Behavioral Instructions?" *Journal of Motor Behavior* 50(3): 312–320.

EPILOGUE

My recent work applies systems thinking to understand the long-term performance of business firms. My previous book *Value Creation Principles* developed the pragmatic theory of the firm, while explaining its benefits for investors, management, boards of directors, businesspeople, regulators, politicians, and students. *Value Creation Principles* and my book-in-progress *Fulcrum Insights: How You Can Generate Big Ideas to Elevate System Performance* (of which this short book is the opening chapter) have their roots in knowledge-building proficiency being the fundamental determinant of a firm's long-term performance.

For an insightful introduction to *Value Creation Principles,* check out Jack Reardon's review below. Jack is the founding editor of the *International Journal of Pluralism and Economics Education* and the author of four books on economics. He has a well-deserved reputation for creatively analyzing economic problems and illuminating innovative ways to achieve economic progress that will lift all boats.

BOOK REVIEW

International Journal of Pluralism and Economics Education
Vol. 11, No. 2, 2020, pp. 214-219
Reviewed by Jack Reardon

Value Creation Principles: The Pragmatic Theory of the Firm
Begins with Purpose and Ends with Sustainable Capitalism
by Bartley J. Madden

Published 2020
by John Wiley & Sons
Hoboken, NJ, 250pp
ISBN: 978119706625 (Hardcover)

Probably my biggest irritation with neoclassical microeconomics has been its stubborn reluctance to understand and investigate the firm as the capitalist economy's basic building block. Indeed, the firm has long been pejoratively referred as the black box, not exactly a compliment for a profession whose jurisdiction is supposedly the economy. When I took my obligatory courses in the theory of the firm, I realised early on that the so-called theory had little to do with the firm; and that you could substitute any entity and obtain the same results. In fact, after these courses I knew less about the firm than I did beforehand. Adding to the frustration was that the world was changing, but the theory of the firm had ossified: its frame of reference and conceptual tools ensconced in the pre-World War One era.[1] The neoclassical theory of the firm became emmeshed in its own deductive and ahistorical logic, as if economics was a 'branch of applied mathematics' [Hodgson (1999), p.8] rather than a social science.

---

1. Lee (2010, p.205) noted that the core theoretical tools of neoclassical theory circa 1900–1910, i.e., scarcity, maximisation, utility and marginal utility, marginal product and the law of diminishing returns, supply and demand curves, the marginal productivity principle of distribution, and the core model of competition have been retained throughout the century".

A long-time objective of mine has been to write a pluralist book on the theory of the firm[2], but alas, founding the *IJPEE*, and three books later on economics education put this project on the proverbial back burner, and then off the stove completely. So I am thrilled that such a book is finally on the market, and that Bart Madden beat me to the punch, for he has written a much better book on the subject than I could have, or anyone else for that matter.

Madden, an independent researcher and prolific author, is that rare polymath who utilizes ideas from many disciplines. He is equally at home in management, finance, economics, medicine, philosophy, and psychology; in fact for Madden, these are not exactly separate silos. He is eager to learn, not to ossify and self-confirm, but to enlighten in order to help make the world a better place. He epitomises erudition, enthusiasm for learning, and an insightful open-mindedness.

Value Creation Principles is based on Madden's 50 years doing financial analysis, valuation model development, and portfolio management; learning how real firms work, the importance of the firm to capitalism, and the essence of sustainability long before the word came in vogue. Madden knows his stuff and he knows his firms.

Reviewing a Bart Madden book has become a pleasurable and enjoyable bi-annual task; and he is rapidly becoming one of my favorite authors. When I reviewed his most recent book (Madden, 2018). I urged him to "please survey our economy and find

---

2. Commemorating Martin Luther and the 500th anniversary of the commencement of the Reformation, I wrote: "Economics must become more inductive and less deductive. One is hard-pressed to find in any economics textbook empirical evidence about how real-world firms behave and how they operate. Instead we find fabricated data based on 19th century prescripts of how firms should behave. If we presume to teach about modern capitalism, we should begin with real world data. (That this is even mentioned underscores how dysfunctional economics has become)" [Reardon, (2017), Thesis #50, p.324].

other areas with a disconnect between technology, democracy, and efficiency (perhaps higher education?) We need your passion, your voice, and your erudition" [Reardon, (2018), p.427]. Thankfully he responded pretty quickly, although this book has been gestating for quite some time.[3]

At only 238 pages of text, most readers will be surprised by the book's brevity. Yeah, Madden says a lot and packs the pages with interesting stuff, yet, his crisp and efficient prose is engaging and inviting, and parts read like a novel (literary, not mystery!) Madden's firms come alive, and just like a good novel, the reader is hooked, wanting to know more.

The book's seven chapters are divided into three parts: a firm's role in society; the pragmatic theory of the firm connects innovation and valuation; and value creation. Part 1, a firm's role in society, lays the groundwork for the book's four themes:

- *Pragmatic*: The book was originally titled *The Pragmatic Theory of the Firm*, then revised prior to publication, while moving pragmatic to the subtitle. Pragmatic (from the Greek word, meaning 'deed') means practical: concerned with facts or actual events. And according to the common dictionary, 'practical' has several nuanced definitions, the most apt here: 'capable of being used or put into effect; useful. "Madden's pragmatic theory of the firm connects the firm's purpose, major activities, and its long-term overall performance, with particular attention to long-term financial performance" (p.30).

- *Knowledge building*: Madden begins his book with the unequivocal statement: "I strongly believe that a firm's long-term performance is a direct result of its knowledge building proficiency" (p.15). Indeed knowledge building provides the foundation for his theory of the firm,

---

3. I also reviewed Madden (2014) in the IJPPE, (Reardon, 2015).

explains how a firm produces value, and the capacity to build knowledge, and differentiates between successful and unsuccessful firms. It is of "paramount importance in determining a firm's survival and prosperity over the long term" (p.34). Knowledge building has five interlocking components: purpose, worldview, perceptions, actions and consequences, and feedback, each of which strongly influences how we build knowledge (p.32). For Madden, "knowledge building and value creation are opposite sides of the same coin" (p.64).

- *Life cycle framework*: focuses on an individual firm delivering economic returns and reinvestment during the four stages of its life cycle: high innovation, competitive fade, maturity, and failing business. This framework, Madden convincingly demonstrates, is more accurate and holistic than traditional valuation measures.

- *Systems thinking*: is a central unifying theme of all Madden's books.[4] Rather than look at one isolated component, as if each were separate entities, systems thinking is about connectedness, about how the whole system works. Systems thinking obviously proffers a different worldview, albeit much more accurate. The pragmatic theory of the firm "applies systems thinking to improve our understanding of firms and our measurement tools, and to upgrade decision-making" (p.222).

Chapter 1 expands on the concept of a pragmatic theory, while also providing a highly readable historical evolution of the theory of the firm, differentiating a pragmatic theory from other theories. As the book's subtitle reads, 'The pragmatic theory of

---

4. In an earlier book, Madden identified (and explained) systems thinking as one of the four core beliefs businesses need to solve complex problems; specifically, "to address the tendency toward an excessive focus on local efficiencies that can easily degrade overall system performance, and to powerfully identify and focus on fixing the key constraints" [Madden, (2014), p.42].

the firm begins with purpose and ends with sustainable capital-ism'. Madden defines a pragmatic firm as "a dynamic system of coordinated activities that evolves as management and employ-ees build knowledge in order to create value for customers" (p.4). While the literature abounds with definitions of a firm's purpose, most are either deductively based, or too narrow (or both), focusing only on one stakeholder, ignoring the well-being of the others and how this interacts to affect the firm's holistic success. For Madden, a pragmatic firm has a four-part purpose rooted in the knowledge building loop:

- communicate a vision to inspire and motivate employ-ees to make the world a better place

- survive and prosper through continual gains in effi-ciency and sustained innovation

- sustain win-win relationships with all the firm's stake-holders

- take care of future generations with a genuine commit-ment to ensure the sustainability of the environment (pp.26–27).

And thus, "knowledge-building proficiency tied to the four-part purpose is a viable route to taking care of future generations" (p.27). Madden's emphasis on sustainability, often missing in the traditional literature, is important and will increase the applicability and reach of his book.

Chapter 2 discusses knowledge building, which not only is an end in itself and a means to increase value, but is also a metric to analyse a firm's success/failure. While each component of knowledge building is critically important, feedback emerges as "hugely important" (p.41) since it "ideally facilitates new knowl-edge building that is critical in directing innovation both for existing products and new products that may significantly differ from existing products" (p.194). Feedback works exceedingly well for Netflix, according to its web page:

> "We believe we will learn faster and be better if we can make giving and receiving feedback less stressful and a normal part of work life. Feedback is a continuous part of how we communicate and work with one another versus an occasional formal exercise...Feedback helps us avoid sustained misunderstandings and the need for rules" (p.187).

In building the knowledge loop Madden calls for humility (economists take notice!), "what we don't know... will open the door wider to deeper understanding" (pp.40–41).

Chapter 3 utilises knowledge-building as a general-purpose analytical metric to explain three important approaches to improving firm performance: Lean Thinking (pioneered by Toyota); the theory of constraints (developed by Eli Goldratt); and Werner Erhard's and Michael Jensen's recent ontological/phenomenological model.

Chapter 4 uses the life cycle framework as the basis for his innovation life-cycle valuation model, to connect a firm's long-term financial performance to its market valuation. The life cycle model, "stripped of any assumptions about risk and return in an assumed equilibrium environment" is superior to the capital asset pricing model (CAPM), touted by mainstream finance (p.218). Finance aficionados will appreciate the helpful addendum 'A research methodology for advancing the life cycle framework', (pp.111–120) just as economists should appreciate Chapter One's historical discussion of the theory of the firm.[5]

---

5. This is not exclusionary by any means. The overall language of these sections is clear and inviting so that all can profit. And by the way, management and investment aficionados can profit from the whole book. A central theme/objective of Madden's research corpus is the dismantling of separate silo thinking; a much-needed objective.

One of the book's more interesting chapters is Chapter 5: 'Intangible assets, brands, and shareholder returns'. Interesting because the topic is often missing in traditional economics texts. Indeed,

> "intangibles play an important role in the generation of a firm's life-cycle performance... and [as such] a prerequisite to analyzing shareholder returns in today's new economy is an insightful understanding of connectivity-enabled innovation, networks, platforms, and the increased importance of hard-to-duplicate intangible assets such as unique human capital (e.g., brands)" (p.122).

Yet, neoclassical economics and traditional accounting[6] are still mired in the ways of the Old Economy (producing physical goods with physical assets) which is problematic since intangible assets (unlike tangible assets such as machinery) typically involve considerable uncertainty as to both the magnitude and duration (life) of future benefits" (p.126). Accounting aficionados (and accounting rule-makers) will appreciate the helpful call to action 'Conceptual roadmap for handling intangible assets' (pp.133–142).

Chapter 6 discusses the firm's organisational structure which is also a source of competitive advantage and value added. The chapter is peppered with the successful case studies of the Haier Group, Morning Star, and Netflix. The Haier Group discussion impugns the common-held assumption that large firms are too big to successfully transform. The typical structure of the New Economy firm is more of a "flattened hierarchical pyramid [with] a structure focused on teams of individuals doing the work of efficiently serving customers" (p.199) creating far more value for customers and other stakeholders.

---

6. For an incisive criticism of traditional accounting with a sustainability twist see Brown and Dillard (2019).

Chapter 7 summarises the book's key take-aways, nicely encapsulated in the following passage:

> "the main theme of the book is that knowledge-building proficiency is the key to long-term value creation by individuals, business units, and firms. A corollary theme is that resources are best allocated by management (including entrepreneurs) less concerned with hierarchal control mechanisms, and instead, intent on developing a knowledge-building culture keyed to innovation and constructive change. Such a culture rewards and motivates those who reveal obsolete assumptions; analyze problems to unravel root causes...that is, fast and effective traversing of the knowledge-building loop" (p.215).

Madden concludes his book by endorsing the nascent movement toward a new discipline of Progress Studies to "study the successful people, organisations, institutions, policies, and cultures that that have arisen to date, and it would attempt to concoct policies and prescriptions that would help improve our ability to generate useful progress in the future" (p.214). In this interesting new discipline, Madden's take is to emphasise the evolutionary process in which "firms build knowledge, create value, and generate progress – a bottom up concrete body of knowledge using the individual firm as the unit of analysis. This book is a step in that direction" (p.238). Indeed it is.

I do not have any criticisms of the book per se (the book was accepted by Madden's first choice, Wiley, without any changes major or minor), which is not surprising given that the book is clearly written, cogently argued, and arguably succeeds at its objective.

While the reviewer's task is to review the book actually written and not the book that the reviewer wanted to read; at the same time, the flip side of writing a succinct and pithy (and much-needed) book on such an important topic is that most readers would have liked this particular topic or that particular topic. This is a cost of writing a short and pithy book; and a natural and expected reaction: like watching a good movie, we are sad to see it end, wanting more. Yet, if Madden were to expand and write a massive Encyclopedia (like many of today's principles of economics textbooks, his book would lose its verve, its passion, its succinctness, and yes, its applicability to understand the rationale and modus operandi of any firm, large or small, local or global.

Who should read this much needed-book that discusses how the capitalist firm creates value, how and why it evolves over its life-stages, its role within capitalism, with a plethora of real-world examples about how real firms actually behave? (I think I just answered my own question: well, everyone.) Every businessperson should read this, not as a rah-rah, motivational book, but as a carefully thought-out book with workable and pragmatic principles of how firms create value based on the author's 50 years in the trenches, and couched in the context of contemporary capitalism. This important book deserves a central place in reconceptualising economics and in a new pluralist curriculum (You need not have a strong background in economics or finance to profit from this book), and it should be mandatory in the economics and MBA curricula.

Bart Madden, I hope you are surveying our economy/society finding other areas, perhaps something more in-depth about knowledge building and the economy: We need your passion, your voice, and your erudition.

Stay tuned!

REFERENCES

Brown, J. and Dillard, J. (2019) "Accounting education, democracy, and sustainability: taking divergent perspectives seriously", *International Journal of Pluralism and Economics Education*, Vol. 10, No. 1, pp.24–45.

Hodgson, G.M. (1999) *Evolutions and Institutions: On Evolutionary Economics and the Evolution of Economics*, Edward Elgar, Cheltenham, UK.

Lee, F. (2010) "A heterodox teaching of neoclassical microeconomic theory", *International Journal of Pluralism and Economics Education*, Vol. 1, No. 3, pp.203–235.

Madden, B. (2014) *Reconstructing Your Worldview: The Four Beliefs You Need to Solve Complex Business Problems*, LearningWhatWorks, Naperville, Illinois.

Madden, B.J. (2018) *Free to Choose Medicine*, 3rd ed., The Heartland Institute, Arlington Heights, Illinois.

Reardon, J. (2015) "Review of *Reconstructing Your Worldview*", *International Journal of Pluralism and Economics Education*, Vol. 6, No. 1, pp.108–110.

Reardon, J. (2017) "Foreword: why economics needs its own reformation: 95 theses", *International Journal of Pluralism and Economics Education*, Vol. 8, No. 4, pp. 319–329.

Reardon, J. (2018) "Review of *Free to Choose Medicine*, 3rd ed.", *International Journal of Pluralism and Economics Education*, Vol. 9, No. 4, pp.425–428.

ABOUT THE AUTHOR

Bartley J. Madden retired as a managing director of Credit Suisse HOLT after a career in investment research and money management that included the founding of Callard Madden & Associates. His early research was instrumental in the development of the cash-flow return on investment (CFROI) valuation framework, which is used today by money management firms worldwide. His book *Value Creation Principles: The Pragmatic Theory of the Firm Begins with Purpose and Ends with Sustainable Capitalism* positions the business firm as the fundamental unit of analysis for economic progress. His website www.LearningWhatWorks.com details a wide range of intellectual interests. An early version of his book *Free to Choose Medicine: Better Drugs Sooner at Lower Cost* was translated into Japanese and played a significant role in Japan's implementation of early, informed access to regenerative medicine drugs. For more, see www.FreeToChooseMedicine.com.